The author and his portable engine at Shibden Hall Folk Museum, Halifax, in 1983.

PORTABLE STEAM ENGINES

Lyndon R. Shearman

Shire Publications Ltd

CONTENTS

Early history 3

Technical developments 6

Mechanical details 11

Portable engines at work 19

Variations and special types 23

Engines in preservation 27

Further reading 30

Places to visit 32

Published in 1995 by Shire Publications Ltd, Cromwell House, Church Street, Princes Risborough, Buckinghamshire HP27 9AA, UK. Copyright © 1986 by Lyndon R. Shearman. First published 1986; reprinted 1995. Shire Album 163. ISBN 0 85263 783 7.

Printed in Great Britain by CIT Printing Services, Press Buildings, Merlins Bridge, Haverfordwest, Dyfed SA61 1XF.

British Library Cataloguing in Publication Data: Shearman, Lyndon R. Portable steam engines. — (Shire album, 163) 1. Portable engines — Great Britain — History I. Title 621.1'5'0941. TJ 710. ISBN 0-85263-783-7.

ACKNOWLEDGEMENTS

The author wishes to thank all those who helped in the production of this book. In particular, illustrations on the following pages are acknowledged to: Michael Clark, cover; George Drake, of the Northern Mill Engine Society, page 31; Halifax Courier, page 1; Ray Hooley, pages 3 (right), 12, 14, 24 (lower); Mike Jones, pages 17 (lower), 21 (lower), 30; Museum of Lincolnshire Life, pages 8, 16, 25; Tony Olive, of Aveling-Barford Ltd, page 7; Trustees of the Science Museum, page 3 (left); the late J. A. Smith, pages 4, 6, 9, 10, 11, 13, 17 (upper), 19, 20, 21 (upper), 22, 23, 24 (upper), 26, 27, 28, 29. Thanks are also due to P. K. Duncombe, of Robey of Lincoln Ltd; Christine Ede; Henry Marshall, of Track-Marshall Ltd; and Jim Moran. The illustrations on pages 2, 5 and 18 are from the author's collection.

COVER: *Ransomes, Sims & Jefferies portable engine number 44126, built in 1938, seen at a rally at Castle Howard in 1975.*

BELOW: *An engraving of a Brown & May portable driving a threshing machine.*

LEFT: *Trevithick's engine supplied to Sir Christopher Hawkins at Trewithen in 1811, used for threshing and now preserved in the Science Museum, London.*
RIGHT: *A classic in portable engine history, Hornsby's engine of 1851 with the cylinders contained within the high-roofed outer firebox. These engines were very economical. Two of the chains below the boiler are 'lock chains', to prevent the forecarriage from turning too far, while the third chain carries a drag shoe which is placed under the rear wheel for braking when going downhill.*

EARLY HISTORY

The portable steam engine is the ancestor of the traction engine. It is a self-contained power unit capable of driving machinery and is mounted on wheels so as to be readily moved about, but it is not self-propelling, requiring to be towed by horse, traction engine or tractor.

The idea of the portable steam engine originated with the Cornishman Richard Trevithick. His experiments with high-pressure steam led him to produce 'whim engines', which were used for winding ore out of the Cornish mines. They were self-contained, readily installed at the head of the mine shaft, and easily moved to another shaft if required. By contrast, the Watt steam engines of the day were huge machines, often house-built (that is, the engine house itself formed the framework of the engine), and while these engines were sometimes moved

from place to place such moves were massive and expensive undertakings. In 1811 Trevithick produced the first of a series of engines intended for agricultural use. It was sold to Sir Christopher Hawkins of Trewithen, and after many years of use was handed to the Science Museum for preservation in 1879.

The development of the threshing machine by Andrew Meikle in Scotland and John Balls in East Anglia provided the impetus for the introduction of steam power into agriculture in the late eighteenth and early nineteenth centuries. Some threshers were driven by horse gins, others by water power, and small machines by hand, but gradually stationary steam engines began to be installed on some of the more prosperous farms. The need began to be felt for a portable threshing machine which could be taken

The author's little Brown and May at Bramham Park Steam Rally, 1981. Note the boiler feed pump driven from the crosshead and the flywheel unusually placed on the right-hand side. Probably built not later than 1868, the very simple lines of the engine are evident. In the early days engines were widely exhibited at agricultural shows, where the judges were obsessed with simplicity, so engine makers, keen to court the judges' favour, made their engines as simple as possible. Brown and May, for example, pointed out in an advertisement in 1866 that their engines were not fitted with feedwater heaters or expansion gear. This engine has no steam jacket either, but the cylinder is lagged with wood.

to the corn stack instead of bringing the corn into a barn where a fixed thresher was installed, and this in turn required the further development of portable steam engines to provide the power. In 1830 Nathan Gough of Salford made a portable engine consisting of a vertical boiler and engine, all mounted on a wooden framework carried on wheels, but in general the disturbed state of agriculture following the Napoleonic Wars prevented much development. It was not until around 1840 that the ideas which had been growing in men's minds began to achieve reality.

More or less simultaneously, portable steam engines, entirely self-contained including boiler, mounted on wheels, and intended primarily for agricultural use, appeared from Alexander Dean of Birmingham, J. R. and A. Ransome of Ipswich, William Tuxford and Sons of Boston and a Mr Howden, also of Boston. Dean's and Ransomes' engines

appeared in 1841, Tuxfords' in 1842, and Howden's in either 1839 or 1841. Ransomes' machine had a rotary engine known as Davies disc type in place of the usual piston and cylinder. While the Davies disc was not widely adopted, portables were, and there followed a period of rapid development. Colbourne Cambridge of Market Lavington, Wiltshire, entered the field in 1843 — he was the inventor of the Cambridge roll still in use on the land today — and he and Dean exhibited at shows against one another throughout the decade.

Clayton and Shuttleworth of Lincoln made their first portable in 1845, and it was the first to have both horizontal boiler and cylinder, though its flywheel was driven through gearing. Previous engines had had vertical or horizontal boiler and vertical or inclined cylinders, while Tuxfords persisted with vertical cylinders with the moving parts enclosed in a lockable sheet-iron box, where they were protected from dust, rain, theft of brasswork or 'meddling spectators'. There was a fear that horizontal cylinders might wear oval, but by the end of the decade the now familiar layout of locomotive-type boiler, horizontal cylinder over the firebox and flywheel mounted on the crankshaft had appeared; Wansbrough said that Richard Bach's engine of 1850 was the first such, but W. J. Hughes claimed that it was Clayton and Shuttleworth's 1848 engine. Other early exhibitors of portable engines included Garrett at Leiston, Suffolk, and Hornsby of Grantham.

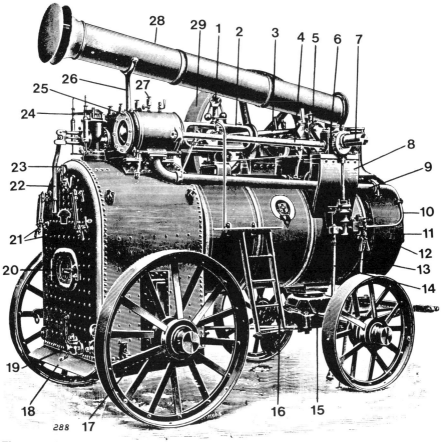

The parts of a portable steam engine.

1 Governor
2 Crosshead guide
3 Connecting rod
4 Tie rod between cylinder block and crankshaft bearing
5 Big end
6 Crankshaft bearing
7 End of crankshaft
8 Crankshaft bearing bracket
9 Exhaust steam pipe
10 Branch pipe taking some exhaust steam for feedwater heating
11 Smokebox
12 Boiler feed pump
13 Return pipe from boiler feed pump
14 Suction pipe to boiler feed pump
15 Swivelling forecarriage
16 Access ladder for oiling and maintenance
17 Ashpan
18 Damper allowing air to enter under fire
19 Drain cock for draining boiler in frosty weather
20 Firehole door
21 Water gauges
22 Regulator lever
23 Steam pressure gauge
24 Two spring balance safety valves
25 Cylinder block
26 Rest for chimney
27 Cylinder oil cup
28 Chimney, folded down
29 Flywheel rim

A Fowler portable shown in a catalogue of 1870.

TECHNICAL DEVELOPMENTS

Having settled down to a thoroughly practical form, the portable engine was rapidly accepted as a commercially useful machine, and it was estimated that thousands were at work in the early 1850s. Improvements were in matters of details, but important details nonetheless. Clayton and Shuttleworth, for example, reduced the coal consumption of their engines from 11.8 pounds (5.23 kg) per horsepower hour in 1849 to only 4.05 pounds (1.8 kg) in 1855.

Boiler pressures crept higher, and boilermaking techniques improved, with rivet holes being drilled instead of punched, plates flanged instead of joined by angle irons, and the plates carefully formed so as to fit snugly together instead of being strained together by cramps and drifts. Wrought iron, from Low Moor or Bowling in West Yorkshire or from Staffordshire, was the only material considered suitable for boilers and fireboxes until the introduction of mild steel in the 1870s; Davey Paxman of Colchester claimed to be the first portable engine maker to use steel fireboxes.

Steam-jacketed cylinders came into general use, and by keeping the cylinder hot the problem of cylinder condensation was avoided, with a saving in fuel. Clayton and Shuttleworth had, in some of their early engines, placed the cylinder in the smokebox to the same good effect, while Hornsby in 1848 had the cylinder within the high-roofed outer firebox, and Cambridge had put the vertical cylinder in the boiler as far back as 1843, but many early engines had no steam jacket on the cylinder. The writer's little Brown and May portable of about 1868 has no steam jacket and on raising steam it is necessary to run the engine with no load to warm the cylinder before the engine will drive a load. Similarly, the engine works at only 40 pounds per square inch (2.8 kg/sq cm) and to drive a load it is necessary to keep the steam pressure well in the thirties. The Low Moor iron boiler and firebox on this engine have lasted remarkably well.

Another important improvement was the introduction of compounding by Garrett in 1880, just preceding its introduction by Fowler in traction engines in 1881. In a single-cylinder engine the steam is used in the cylinder once and is then exhausted up the chimney. In a compound engine there are two cylinders and the steam is used twice, first in the high-pressure cylinder and then in the low-pressure cylinder, before being exhausted up the chimney. By this means more of the heat energy in the steam is converted into useful work. The idea of compounding was not new, dating back to the late eighteenth century, but it had only recently been made into a practicable proposition; for example, the first compound railway locomotive had

Aveling and Porter portable number 3338, built in 1894, photographed in 1976 when it was bought back by Aveling-Barford Ltd from Jack Pierson of Darlington. Aveling and Porter made portables from 1864 to 1920, and this engine shows many features of a typical portable. Note the pulley on the crankshaft, smaller than the flywheel, for driving machines which needed to run slowly. The exhaust steam from the cylinder passes through the pipe along the boiler top, with a branch pipe taking some steam for feed water heating to the boiler feed pump. The feed pump has a bypass and works continuously while the engine is running, unlike those usually fitted to Aveling road engines. The raised-top firebox gives extra water and steam space around the fire where it is most useful, and this slightly raised position of the cylinder helps put it in line with the crankshaft. The raised-top firebox was not used on very large portables, however, since a flush-topped firebox was reckoned to give a stronger boiler structure, with no discontinuity between firebox and boiler. The engine's chimney folds down when not in use to rest in the iron crutch on top of the cylinder block. The whistle was used for signalling starting and finishing times and meal breaks, or to call for water, while its modern use is for joining in the choruses of whistles at rallies. Notice how placing the rear wheels alongside the firebox and setting back the forecarriage under the boiler gives a shorter wheelbase, making the engine more manoeuvrable.

A Robey portable of 200 brake horsepower, the largest size of portable made, with an empty weight of over 42 tons.

appeared only in 1876. Compounding could effect useful savings in fuel and water, but the simple engine was never superseded. Where cheap fuel, such as straw, was used, and where water did not have to be carried long distances, there was not the incentive to pay the extra first cost for a compound or to put up with the extra complications. In the smaller sizes of engine the amount of fuel consumed was not great, so the savings to be gained were much less, and so compounding was usually applied only in the larger sizes. A large single-cylinder engine with its heavy reciprocating parts could cause problems with balancing, so the very large sizes were made as either compounds or two-cylinder simple engines. The largest portables of all were of 200 brake horsepower by Robey and Company of Lincoln.

The conventional cylinder-over-firebox layout had the advantage of keeping the flywheel and other moving parts away

from the driver — a belt fastener can deliver a nasty blow to the unwary. Early traction engines, such as Thomas Aveling's, retained the portable engine layout, but it was quickly found that in tractions it was handier to have the crankshaft over the firebox. Not only did this enable the chain drive then in use to be shortened, but the driver could pull the flywheel round by hand to put the engine into gear or pull the crank off dead centre on starting. In portables these considerations were unimportant and so the original layout was retained to the end except in a few cases such as electric light engines with a dynamo mounted ahead of the smokebox and belt-driven from the flywheel, or Fowler portables, which had the crankshaft over the firebox. Fowler was never a large maker of portables, and there is a legend that John Fowler and Brown and May of Devizes were friends in their younger days and established a gentlemen's agreement that Fowler would not make portables while Brown and May would not make steam ploughing tackle, which was Fowler's speciality. Fowler was born at Melksham, not far from Devizes, and Brown and May concentrated on portables throughout the nineteenth century, so there may be some truth in the legend, and the Fowler portable layout may have been used so as not to offend Brown and May.

Portable engine makers were always conscious of the need for engines to be capable of delivery to remote areas, including dismantling and re-erection en route. Exports of engines were important, particularly during the agricultural depression in Britain in the 1880s and 1890s. Wansbrough outlined the technique of taking an engine across a river by removing easily detachable parts, plugging all openings in the boiler and floating the boiler across using lashed-on timbers to give buoyancy. There arose, therefore, the concept of the detachable engine, whereby portable engines could be readily taken to pieces and re-erected with the minimum of skilled labour. To this end, flat-footed cylinder blocks were placed on pressed or cast saddles fixed to the boiler, the flat joints being easily remade. Detachable crankshaft bearings were similarly bolted to their flat-faced brackets. Davey Paxman and Dodman made a type of portable on which the complete engine, bed and all, was detachable and could even be used, with a steam supply, remote from its boiler.

A portable engine by William Allchin and Company Ltd, Northampton.

ABOVE: *This partly stripped Davey Paxman shows how the crankshaft bearings are carried on pressed steel brackets and tied to the cylinder block by tie-rods. The engine was photographed in 1954 in a contractor's yard in Aberdeen.*

BELOW: *Working parts of a Ruston double-cylinder portable. The Ruston 'patent steam stay', running from crankshaft bearing to cylinder block, can be clearly seen.*

Marshall number 79936, under scrutiny at Kendal Steam Rally in 1982. Marshall made about 22,000 portables in all, the first in 1852 and the last in 1946.

MECHANICAL DETAILS

As engine sizes and powers increased, so too did the force of the piston thrusts. The to-and-fro piston thrusts placed racking strains on the cylinder block and crankshaft brackets, so that the bolts holding these parts to the boiler could work loose. Once the bolts became slightly loose, water and steam could leak past them, causing corrosion which enlarged the holes, thereby making the bolts looser still. This same problem had plagued traction engine designers and had led to Aveling's invention of hornplates, but this invention was not applicable to portables. The immediate solution was to provide strong tie-rods between the cylinder block and crankshaft bracket to absorb the piston thrusts and relieve the holding-down bolts of stress. Unfortunately this simple solution brought with it another problem. As the boiler expanded

as steam was raised, so the tie-rod remained cool and did not expand. This placed heavy thermal stresses on the tie-rods, boiler and holding-down bolts; in effect the tie-rod was trying to prevent the boiler from expanding, while the boiler as it expanded was trying to stretch the tie-rod. This was not a satisfactory solution, and it was increasingly felt that the boiler had enough to do in withstanding the pressure of the steam inside it without having to act as a frame for the engine parts as well.

Ruston Proctor brought out a neat solution to the problem with their 'patent steam stay'. This consisted of a tie-rod arranged in the usual way to absorb the stresses of the engine, but the tie-rod or stay was a hollow tube, and a small pipe connected this tubular stay to the boiler. Thus, as steam was raised in the boiler, so the tubular stay also filled with steam and became hot, and it expanded as the boiler did. There were no stresses due to expansion between the boiler and the stay because the two expanded together, and yet the stay could still absorb all the piston thrusts.

Most makers, however, adopted a different, though equally neat solution. A tie-rod was placed between the cylinder block and the crankshaft bearing in the usual way, but the bearing was in turn mounted on its supporting bracket in such a way that it could slide lengthways.

When the boiler warmed up and expanded, the tie-rod remained the same length, and the crankshaft bearing was free to slide a little on its bracket to take up the difference so that there were no thermal stresses. The tie-rod itself absorbed the piston thrusts and the boiler was relieved of such stresses.

Garrett, however, fitted no tie-rods of any sort, maintaining that they did not provide the necessary support. Instead they used very strong crankshaft brackets bolted to a special saddle, which in turn was fixed to the boiler. The Garrett firm

A Ruston Proctor single-cylinder piston-valve engine with spark arrester chimney. In the twentieth century many makers produced piston-valve engines in an attempt to secure greater economy. Higher boiler pressures were used, usually 140 to 180 pounds per square inch (9.8 to 12.6 kg/sq cm) and this required a high standard of boilermaking; for example the corners of the firebox plates are flanged to a wide radius to help prevent cracks forming. Great care has been taken with the lagging to retain heat and conserve fuel — the firebox top, cylinder cover and cylinder base all being lagged. Useful economies were made with these higher-pressure engines, even more so when compounding and superheating were applied, and the most efficient portable would burn less than 2 pounds (0.9 kg) of coal per brake horsepower hour, a performance equal to the best railway locomotive. Despite this, the old-fashioned slide-valve single-cylinder engine continued to be made, for the attributes of simplicity and reliability were strong virtues in portable engines.

A Marshall 'Britannia' portable, number 88270, built in 1936, with a circular firebox, at Driffield Rally in 1983.

always preferred to use its own methods.

Most portables were fitted with feedwater heaters, whereas most traction engines were not. When a boiler is steaming continuously, water has to be fed into it to replace that boiled away, and on a portable this was usually achieved by means of an engine-driven pump under the control of the driver. When cold water is fed into a hot boiler, however, several ill effects can follow. First, the cold water tends to cool the boiler, reducing the steam pressure; this is akin to pouring cold water into a boiling kettle, sending it off the boil. Second, the chilling effect can set up stresses in the boiler plates, and, third, the additional oxygen in the water can cause corrosion of the plates. A feedwater heater takes waste heat and uses it to warm the feedwater almost to boiling point, so mitigating these ill effects and at the same time turning to good use heat which would otherwise be wasted, effecting a saving of fuel. On a portable engine the waste heat comes from the exhaust steam which would otherwise be thrown away up the chimney. The exhaust steam runs through a pipe along the boiler top, but a branch pipe takes some of this steam for feedwater heating. The boiler feed pump works continuously and returns surplus water to the water barrel which stands by the engine, and in the return pipe the steam is condensed, so that the water in the barrel gradually warms up. Any oil in the exhaust steam floats to the top of the water in the barrel, where it can be skimmed off so that it will not enter the boiler.

A few makers, including Marshall, Garrett and Robey, made engines with condensers. These engines condensed all the exhaust steam so that the condensate could be fed back into the boiler. This saved fuel, Marshall claiming a saving of 12 to 20 per cent over a non-condensing engine. On a non-condensing engine the exhaust steam passing up the chimney created the draught on the fire, but on a condensing engine an extra-long chimney had to be provided to create the draught.

When an engine is working, the steam passing into the cylinders contains tiny

A Hornsby double-cylinder portable of 1885 with a cylindrical firebox capable of burning logs. A number of makers used cylindrical fireboxes, but Davey Paxman disapproved of them and made a log-burning engine with the usual locomotive-type boiler with a specially lengthened firebox. Paxman's catalogue of 1913 says: 'The circular-firebox portable is far from being as efficient as the loco type . . . The circular-firebox boiler cannot be forced like the loco type, and it is also very liable to prime.' Nevertheless circular fireboxes were made by many makers from the 1860s to the 1930s.

droplets of water. The steam in this condition is said to be saturated. As the engine works, the steam gives up some of its heat, and this heat energy is converted into useful work. When saturated steam gives up heat, some of the steam has to condense into water drops because saturated steam has, in effect, no heat to spare. If some of the steam condenses in the cylinder, then more steam has to come from the boiler to replace it, and so the engine is using more steam than it should. Suppose, however, that the steam is taken from the boiler and passed through heated tubes. Any water droplets in the steam are dried out and the steam becomes very hot and dry, and in this condition it is said to be superheated. If this principle is applied to a steam engine and superheated steam is fed into the cylinders instead of saturated, then the superheated steam has heat to spare and it can give up heat to be converted into

useful work without any condensation taking place in the cylinder. In addition, superheating causes the steam to expand, so that a given volume of saturated steam produced by the boiler will produce an increased volume of superheated steam to be fed into the cylinders. In other words, if the cylinders require a certain volume of steam, then the boiler has less work to do in providing that steam.

The principle of superheating was widely used on railway engines and stationary engines, but not so much on portables. Nevertheless, Garrett made a range of superheater portables, and tests carried out on them showed excellent economy of fuel and water. Marshall, too, made superheater portables and they also obtained excellent results. On these portables steam from the boiler was passed through coiled tubes in the smokebox before being fed into the cylinders, so that the steam was super-

14

heated by the heat of the flue gases from the fire, heat which would otherwise have been wasted up the chimney. Superheating was thus very nearly a case of something for nothing, although because of the dryness and temperature of the steam special oil had to be used to lubricate the cylinder. For a superheater to be effective the engine has to be working continuously so that the superheater coils can get very hot. On a road locomotive, for example, working uphill and down, a superheater would cool on the downhill runs, losing some of its effectiveness, and similarly a steam roller, working intermittently as required by its road gang, would not benefit much from superheating. A portable, however, driving its load continuously, was a good prospect for superheating. Nevertheless, despite all the good test results, superheating in portables did not become common, although it marks an important stage in development.

A good deal of thought was given to firebox design. A portable engine has two fireboxes, one inside the other. The fire burns in the inner firebox, and the space between the inner and outer fireboxes is filled with water. The curved surfaces of the boiler can withstand the steam pressure by virtue of their shape, but the flat surfaces, the sides and crown, of the firebox require to be strengthened by means of screwed stays. Putting in firebox stays required extra work when the boiler was made, and stays needed replacing if they corroded during the boiler's life, so it was an advantage if they could be dispensed with. Both Garrett in 1876 and Marshall in 1910 produced designs of a firebox with corrugations to give the strength to enable the crown stays to be done away with. Moreover, the absence of stays made the crown easier to keep clean, and this helped to prolong its life. At Robey and Company a special type of firebox crown stay was developed by Dyson and Wansbrough, the author of *The Portable Steam Engine*. This system also gave ample space for cleaning, as well as giving the firebox extra strength in the vertical direction.

There was a fashion for wet-bottom fireboxes, where the water space around the firebox was continued below the ashpan. The idea was to give extra heating surface, but it made a boiler more complicated and expensive to make, so the idea did not become popular, but a variation on the theme, the cylindrical firebox, was more widely adopted. This firebox was in the form of a horizontal cylinder let into the end of the boiler, so that the firebox was surrounded by water above and below. It gave a greater ground clearance than a conventional firebox, a useful asset where an engine was to work in undeveloped country, and by its length it allowed the use of logs for fuel. Cylindrical fireboxes were made by Marshall, Robey, and Brown and May, and also by E. S. Hindley in some very small two-wheel portables. Ransomes had taken the idea further in the 1860s under the patent of Bidall and Balk, the inner firebox and smokebox tubeplate being bolted into place instead of riveted so that firebox, tubes and tubeplate could be withdrawn for cleaning, inspection or repair. Other makers later took up this idea, while Ransomes, curiously, laid it aside.

When a portable engine was working, the load it drove might vary, but the engine was still required to run at a steady speed. A governor was therefore provided to control the engine and keep the speed steady, whether the load was heavy or light. The earliest governors were of the slow-speed type, wherein large heavy spherical weights suspended from arms were rotated by the engine. If the load lessened and the speed rose, the weights flew out by centrifugal force, and a linkage connected to the arms closed a throttle valve which reduced the supply of steam to the engine, allowing it to slow down to its correct speed again. Later, high-speed governors were used, with smaller weights driven at a higher speed acting directly on a throttle valve, and these responded much more quickly to a change in load. These high-speed governors originated in the United States in the 1860s but were little used in Britain until the 1890s. The Pickering was the most widely used type, and some of the older engines had their original governors replaced by Pickerings.

On compound engines in particular it was popular for a time to use what were known as expansion gears for governing. The governor still consisted of revolving flyweights, but the method of controlling the amount of steam fed to the cylinders was different. Instead of closing off the steam supply by a throttle valve, steam was allowed to enter the cylinder block unchecked, and the amount of steam admitted per piston stroke was controlled by the governor. On light load only a small quantity of steam was admitted to the cylinder at the beginning of each piston stroke, and this steam expanded as it drove the piston back. This was a very efficient way of working, for the steam as it expanded gave up a greater proportion of its heat to be converted into useful work. Throttling the steam was more wasteful, the steam having to force its way through the partly closed throttle valve. At least, that was the theory. In practice engines with expansion gear, or cut-off governing as it was known, were more complicated and more expensive to buy and maintain, while their greater economy of fuel was significant only when the engine was driving a light load,

when less fuel was consumed anyway. The simple throttle governor therefore always retained a good share of the market.

Some portables were made with reversing gear so they could run in either direction as required, but again this introduced extra complication, and the usual method of reversing the drive was by crossing the driving belt. With a crossed belt, the driven machine will run in the opposite direction to the engine.

Most portables had their moving parts out in the open, and every bearing had to be lubricated by the driver before starting work and at intervals during the day, so efficient lubrication depended on the diligence of the driver. A number of portable engines were made with working parts completely enclosed in an oil bath. Garrett made some engines like this, while Sentinel of Shrewsbury made a type of portable based on their high-pressure boiler and enclosed engine which had proved successful on their steam wagons, but none of these types became popular, for portable users were

796

16

ABOVE: *A threshing scene near Driffield, Humberside, probably during the last years of the nineteenth century. A Marshall portable provides the power, while the 'penny-farthing' shows the personal transport of the day.*

OPPOSITE: *A Robey portable with automatic expansion gear, in which the governor alters the cut-off as the load varies. Many Robeys, such as this one, had a screw-type stop-valve or regulator, worked by the L-shaped handle. The regulator on a portable is not used like that on a traction engine, being used only for starting and stopping; the governor controls the speed and the engine is run with the regulator fully open. However, good practice demands that a screw-type regulator, if opened full, should then be closed half a turn so that it cannot stick in the fully open position.*

RIGHT: *A portable engine and its proud driver, busy threshing at Llangernyw, North Wales. Note the rag wrapped around the iron crutch in which the chimney rests when folded down, to stop the chimney chafing and wearing through.*

reluctant to abandon the traditional form of engine which had served so well for so long.

The piston in its cylinder was lubricated by oil introduced right into the cylinder, at first by various types of oil cup and later on by small oil pumps driven off any convenient part of the engine to give a regular and more reliable supply of cylinder oil. In the very early days cylinders were lubricated with animal fats, which smelled abominably when hot, while other parts of the engine, bearings, etcetera, were lubricated with castor oil. Mineral oils came into use around the 1860s, displacing both fat and castor oil, and have remained in use ever since. Cylinder oil is very thick and has to be warmed before it will pour easily, and engines were often seen with a tin of cylinder oil resting on top of the firebox to keep warm.

If a bearing ran hot the driver might add a little graphite or flowers of sulphur to the oil as a palliative, but the drivers had to be resourceful to work an engine out on a site without workshop facilities. Oil and soot mixed together made a black coating for the chimney and smokebox, where the paint of the time would not stand the heat, and smokebox ash or soot on a damp cloth made a brass polish. Joints could be made with a jointing paste composed of iron filings and sal ammoniac (ammonium chloride) if the joint was intended to be permanent, or with red lead and cotton if it might have to be renewed from time to time. If the coal used had a tendency to clinker, some broken firebrick spread over the firebars would help to keep the fire clean by soaking up the molten clinker.

Standard portable engines were designed to use coal as fuel, but many other fuels were burned. A coal-burning engine will usually burn wood readily, but there were engines made with extra-large fireboxes specifically for burning wood. With some modification other fuels could also be burned, such as sawdust, straw or vegetable refuse such as bagasse (the pulp left from the crushing of sugar cane) — the Victorians were very conscious of the advantages of using waste products for fuel. Oil fuel systems could also be provided for burning crude oil.

These drawings show how a portable or semi-portable engine can be placed with its firebox over a stepped firegrate in a brick pit so that poor quality fuels can be burned. The left-hand drawing shows a stepped grate for burning sawdust, and the right-hand drawing shows a firegrate for burning husks. 1 inner firebox; 2 outer firebox; 3 boiler tubes taking smoke and hot gases to smokebox; 4 firehole door closed off; 5 chute through which fuel is fed; 6 firegrate in the form of a flight of steps, down which the fuel falls, burning as it goes; 7 brickwork foundation on which the engine's firebox rests; 8 ashpit.

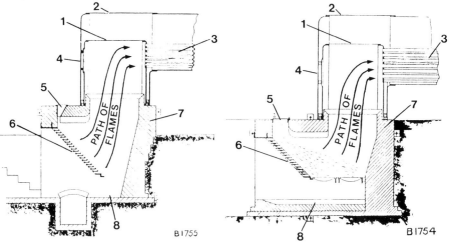

B 1755   B 1754

18

A Marshall portable at work in Mexico. On the right is the owner of the farm with his sons and the priest who officiated at the ceremony when the machine began work.

PORTABLE ENGINES AT WORK

The principal use for portable engines was driving threshing machines. Many engines were exported, the vast corn-growing areas of eastern Europe and Russia being very large markets. Portables were produced in large numbers in comparison with traction engines, so that they were the main product for many engine builders. In Britain threshing by contract was the rule, with portable engine and thresher being hauled by horses from farm to farm. The general tendency, however, was towards traction engines hauling their own threshers, but some portables continued to drive threshers well into the twentieth century, especially in areas where a traction engine would have been unmanageable.

It was not long after its introduction, however, that it was realised how useful a machine the portable was, and it was given other jobs besides threshing. Within agriculture it was used for sawing timber, pumping water, chopping up hay, and so on. In forestry it was widely used for driving sawmills, while the construction industry also took it up, and as early as 1868 it was noted as being in use for pumping water, mixing mortar, moulding bricks and hoisting stones; in later years it was also used for driving tarmacadam and asphalt mixers and stonecrushers. It was used for driving small factories, being more easily installed than a stationary engine; the Ravensthorpe Engineering Company, where John McLaren worked before setting up J. and H. McLaren with his brother Henry, at one time had a portable engine driving its works.

In the early days portables were used for driving windlasses for the early 'roundabout' steam ploughing tackles,

19

ABOVE AND BELOW: *Marshall portables powering threshing machinery in Australia.*

wherein a plough was hauled to and fro across the field by ropes. These roundabout tackles, since they required only a portable engine for power, continued to be used for many years after the more expensive double-engine ploughing system had become firmly established. A picturesque job sometimes done in Victorian times was the driving of apple presses operated by travelling cider makers, who moved from farm to farm pressing the farmers' harvests of apples. Canal companies used portables for driving water pumps during canal repair jobs, the engine standing either on the towpath or in a boat. Other unusual jobs found by portables included supplying steam to cook animal food, driving well-boring

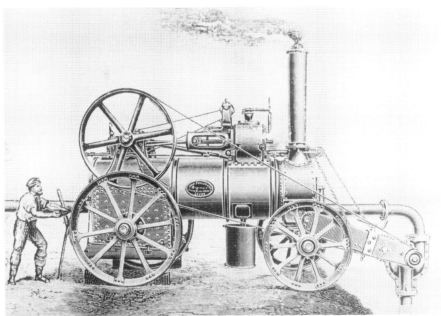

ABOVE: *A Fowler portable driving an engine-mounted centrifugal pump. The pump and its bracket can be hoisted up in front of the smokebox when moving the engine.*

BELOW: *A portable engine and sawbench set up to help with the clearing of a wood for pasture at Llanelidan, North Wales, around 1900. This picture shows a typical sawing gang.*

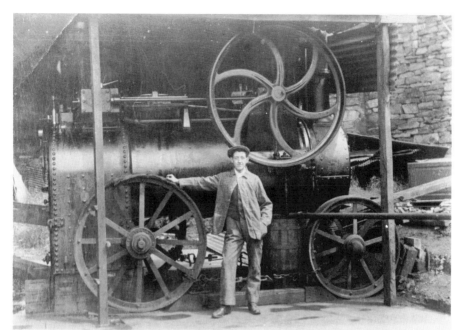

ABOVE: *A Ruston Proctor working at Batley with its driver, Racy Hampshire, in 1911. The engine's task is not known, but the belt drive can just be seen going off to the left. The forecarriage is unusually placed under the smokebox and the flywheel is on the right.*
BELOW: *A Ruston Proctor double-cylinder portable of 1903 working in a malt kiln at Barnby Dun, Doncaster, in 1951.*

equipment, and powering a winch for hauling a descaling device through sewers.

The traction engine never completely replaced the portable, for sound economic reasons. Where, for example, an engine was moved only every few months, as in forestry or construction, it made sense to use a portable, which was much cheaper to buy than a traction. Consequently portables continued to be made alongside tractions and remained in production on a small scale after traction engine production had ceased. Robey and Company even had portables on offer into the 1960s.

VARIATIONS AND SPECIAL TYPES

A variation of the common portable engine was the semi-portable. This was, in effect, a portable without carrying wheels, being supported on stands under the smokebox and firebox, the stand under the firebox forming the ashpan. Except that it was without carrying wheels, the semi-portable was just like a portable. It was used for driving factories, mills and so on, in which use it would not require to be moved around. A variant of the semi-portable was the undertype or semi-fixed engine, where the cylinders were placed below the smokebox, with the crankshaft and the other moving parts below the boiler. Channel iron frames running from firebox to smokebox provided support for the moving parts and formed a foundation for the whole engine.

Another variety of portable engine was the vertical-boilered type, usually made

A Ruston Proctor at Bruntcliffe, near Morley, believed to have been used for sterilising soil, about 1944. Note the massive flat-topped saddle upon which the cylinder block rests. Rustons used to put the entire boiler in a planing machine, to machine the face of the saddle and the seats for the crankshaft bearings at one setting, thus making a very strong and accurate form of construction with the additional advantage that the engine could be readily dismantled and re-erected.

ABOVE: *A Marshall piston-valve portable, number 78074, at Ossett, owned by the West Riding County Council and unusually fitted with a canopy. WRCC had a fleet of portables which were used for driving stone crushers on road repair jobs.*

LEFT: *An unusual portable made by Hornsby in 1890.*

A Robey semi-fixed engine. Usage of such terms as 'semi-fixed' and 'semi-portable' varied from maker to maker.

in small sizes. A frame of some sort was provided, the cylinders being usually vertical and mounted on the side of the boiler, and the whole was placed on carrying wheels. It will be recalled that Nathan Gough's portable of 1830 had a vertical boiler. A little vertical-boilered engine still in existence in County Durham was used for running in threshing machines after overhaul; the engine was belted up to the machine and left running all day so that the new bearings could bed in properly.

Another relative of the portable engine was the portable boiler, simply a locomotive-type boiler mounted on wheels. Because there were no moving parts there could be no engine-driven pump for feeding water into the boiler, so an injector had to be provided instead. In later years many portables and some traction engines were stripped of their engine parts and were used for supplying steam for sterilising soil and other purposes.

A number of specialised types of portable engine were devised for use on the fairground. About 1865 a Mr Soame of Norfolk first used a small portable for driving a roundabout, and within a short time Frederick Savage of King's Lynn was producing engines specially for fairground use. Common portables were used by showmen, but they found it inconvenient to have to haul a portable around along with their other loads, and the familiar showman's road locomotive was evolved both to haul loads and to provide electric power. At the same time a special type of portable engine, the centre engine, was evolved for driving roundabouts.

The centre engine was very compact and was placed within the centre of the ride, with a flue leading to the centre pole, which formed the chimney. These were double-cylinder engines so as to be able to start the ride easily, and a small vertical single-cylinder engine was placed on the smokebox to drive the organ. Being very small, these engines were often pushed to the limit. A showman once recalled how, as a boy, he used to drive his father's centre engine and at busy times had great difficulty in keeping steam up, so he used to shut off the organ engine, but it was never very long before his father would come over wanting to know why the organ was not playing.

Electric light engines were used by showmen in the very early days of electricity on the fairground and had their own dynamo, the whole being mounted in a truck to form a self-contained portable electricity generator. They were made by Savage, Foster and Thomas Green but were rapidly displaced by showmen's road locomotives, as the electric light engine was yet another load to be hauled about. A few survive in preservation.

An odder variant was the type of engine used to drive the swingboats known as steam yachts. The cars were swung by chains driven from the engine crankshaft, the crank making slightly less than a half revolution at full swing. At full stroke the engine valves were worked automatically but for starting and stopping the valves were worked by hand, and an experienced driver could work two sets of valve gear, one for a yacht starting up and the other for a yacht slowing down, each motion being independent of the other but having to be timed exactly to the motion of its car.

A rare portable made by the Farmers Foundry Company of Great Ryburgh, Norfolk. Seen at the sale of the late Tom Paisley's property at Holywell, Cambridgeshire, in 1980, this compound engine has the cranks set at 180 degrees instead of the usual 90 degrees.

Foster portable number 13208 lying derelict in Yorkshire.

ENGINES IN PRESERVATION

With the decline of commercial steam and the growth of the steam preservation movement, some portables found a new and assured future with enthusiastic owners and were to be found at rallies alongside other classes of engine in pristine condition. Even when the preservation movement had become well established, portables still sometimes went for scrap, but it is hoped that that has now come to an end. As rallies progressed from unsuitable activities, such as traction engine racing, to a more realistic presentation of engines, including working demonstrations, so portables were enabled to take a greater part by powering such displays.

On the rally field, the portable is the most accessible to the public of all classes of engine, for the firebox and boiler fittings are not hidden behind or above the tender. People can see the water bobbing up and down in the water gauge, and they can see the fire and feel its heat

as the driver puts on a shovelful of coal.

For the driver, a portable has its own characteristics, which may be unfamiliar to someone more used to road engines. A portable does not shake its fire down as does a traction, so the driver must be careful to keep his fire evenly spread, and if the engine does not steam so easily it may be that ashes are beginning to choke the grate and the fire needs cleaning. When an engine is moved about under steam, the driver has to be sure before moving that there is sufficient water in the boiler to keep the firebox crown covered if the engine is taken downhill, for a portable does not carry its own water supply with it and the driver cannot pump more water in if required. Setting an engine to the machine it is to drive, so that the flywheel and belt pulley are in line, can be difficult with a portable simply because the engine is not self-moving; a traction engine can be easily shunted if

ABOVE: *A Clayton and Shuttleworth single cylinder portable, number 48750, at the Tom Paisley sale in 1980.*

LEFT: *A Burrell portable, number 1475, at Tom Paisley's sale in 1980.*

Marshall number 38318 at Upper Denby Rally, Denby Dale, in 1981. Bad weather had caused muddy conditions, but a portable, once set up, is not too hampered by mud provided there is somewhere dry for the driver to stand and preferably some straw laid on the ground under the driving belt to prevent it from getting dirty if it should come off. Setting up and moving away can, however, be hard work.

the lining up is not quite right, but a portable driver has to get it right first time to save the need for manhandling.

Portables have a charm of their own, and the writer's engine always draws a crowd of interested people around it. This engine has, despite its small size and great age, successfully driven stone crushers and corn mills. It has taken part not only in rallies but also in various shows, where it has attracted plenty of attention. After about sixty years of work, followed by forty years of dereliction, this engine was rebuilt by the late Roger Wyeld of Norfolk, and since then has brought a great deal of pleasure to many people. Its story typifies the way portable engines have given great service all over the world.

FURTHER READING

Bonnett, H. *Farming with Steam.* Shire Publications, 1974; reprinted 1995.
Bonnett, H. *Traction Engines.* Shire Publications, 1985; reprinted 1993.
Gilford, F. H. *The Traction Engine.* Oakwood Press, 1952.
Haining, J., and Tyler, C. *Ploughing by Steam.* Model and Allied Publications, 1970.
(Much detail about roundabout ploughing systems powered by portables.)
Hughes, W. J. *A Century of Traction Engines.* Percival Marshall, 1959.
Johnson, Brian. *Steam Traction Engines, Wagons and Rollers.* Blandford Press, 1971.
Lane, M. *The Story of Britannia Iron Works.* Michael Lane, 1992.
National Traction Engine Club. *Steaming* (special portable engine edition). 1967.
Rolt, L. T. C. *Victorian Engineering.* Pelican Books, 1970.
Turntable Enterprises. *Portable Agricultural Engines.* 1972. (A reprint of part of Bourne's *Catechism of the Steam Engine*, 1868.)
Wansbrough, W. D. *The Portable Steam Engine.* 1912. The classic contemporary work on portables.
Whitehead, R. A. *Garrett's of Leiston.* Model and Allied Publications, 1963.
Williams, M. *Steam Power in Agriculture.* Blandford Press, 1977.

An early Marshall portable, with threshing machinery and the threshing team, near Llanfachraeth, near Dolgellau, Wales.

JOHN PICKLES & SON,

Saw Mill Engineers & Wood-Working Machinists,

HEBDEN BRIDGE, ENGLAND.

TELEGRAMS:
PICKLES, ENGINEERS, HEBDEN BRIDGE.

TELEPHONE No. 12.

IMPROVED PORTABLE STEAM ENGINE, with Single or Double Cylinders.

A P.

A portable offered by John Pickles and Son of Hebden Bridge, probably around the beginning of the twentieth century, when Pickles were also involved in steam wagon manufacture. Certain features of the engine show it is actually a Ruston Proctor, in particular the steam connection to the stay between cylinder and crankshaft bearing, the Ruston transfer on the boiler with the name omitted, the maker's plate on the firebox frontplate, and the design of the boiler feed pump, so presumably Pickles acted as agents for Rustons. The engine has been identified as a Ruston class PDN.

PLACES TO VISIT

Most portable engines are owned by private individuals and are best seen in public at steam rallies, which are held during the summer throughout the British Isles. The *Rally List*, published each February by the National Traction Engine Club, lists many of the year's forthcoming rallies and their organisers and is available from Tourist Board offices. Organisers cannot guarantee that any particular engine or type of engine will attend their rallies, since taking vintage steam engines around the country can be fraught with problems.

Portable or semi-portable engines, or connected items, can be seen at the following, amongst other places. Intending visitors are advised to find out the times of opening and whether the items concerned are on display before making a special journey.

Amberley Chalk Pits Museum, Houghton Bridge, Amberley, Arundel, West Sussex BN18 9LT. Telephone: 01789 831370.

Beamish: The North of England Open Air Museum, Beamish, Stanley, County Durham DH9 0RG. Telephone: 01207 231811.

Bicton Park Countryside Collection, East Budleigh, Budleigh Salterton, Devon EX9 7DP. Telephone: 01395 568465.

Birmingham Museum of Science and Industry, Newhall Street, Birmingham, West Midlands B3 1RZ. Telephone: 0121-236 1022.

Blackgang Sawmill, Blackgang Chine, Ventnor, Isle of Wight PO38 2HN. Telephone: 01983 730330.

Blists Hill Open Air Museum, Madeley, Telford, Shropshire TF8 7AW. Telephone: 01952 586063. (Very small portable made from a variety of parts, including Green's economiser engine.)

Bressingham Live Steam Museum, Bressingham, Diss, Norfolk IP22 2AB. Telephone: 0137988 382 or 386.

British Engineerium, Nevill Road, Hove, East Sussex BN3 7QA. Telephone: 01273 559583 or 554070.

Easton Farm Park, Easton, Woodbridge, Suffolk IP13 0EQ. Telephone: 01728 746475.

Klondyke Mill Steam Museum, Draycott-in-the-Clay, Staffordshire. (Very rare engine by Uriah Nicholls, successor to Nathan Gough, who made very early portables.)

The Long Shop, Main Street, Leiston, Suffolk IP16 4ES. Telephone: 01728 830590. This museum, set up in part of the former Garrett works, includes the workshop, built in 1852 for the production of portable engines.)

Museum of English Rural Life, University of Reading, Whiteknights, Reading, Berkshire RG6 2AG. Telephone: 01734 318660. (In addition to its Clayton portable, this museum has a vast collection of archives of engine makers.)

Museum of Lincolnshire Life, The Old Barracks, Burton Road, Lincoln LN1 3LY. Telephone: 01522 528448. (In addition to portable engines, this museum also contains archives of some of the Lincolnshire engine makers.)

Science Museum, Exhibition Road, South Kensington, London SW7 2DD. Telephone: 0171-938 8000.

Scottish Agricultural Museum, Ingliston, by Edinburgh EH28 8NB. Telephone: 0131-333 2674.

Suffolk Record Office, County Hall, Ipswich, Suffolk IP24 2JS. Telephone: 01473 264541. (Here are kept the archives of Garretts of Leiston.)

Welsh Folk Museum, St Fagans, Cardiff, South Glamorgan CF5 6XB. Telephone: 01222 569441.